Revised
Practice in
Music Theory

Josephine Koh

Grade 5

Based on the music theory syllabus of the Associated Board of the Royal Schools of Music

Published by
Wells Music Publishers
29A Binjai Park
Singapore 589831

Copyright 2007 © by Wells Music Publishers
ISBN 981-05-6610-7

Reprinted in 2010

First edition published in 2000 © by Music Plaza Pte Ltd
Second edition published in 2007 © by Wells Music Publishers

Cover design by Lee Kowling
Typesetting by Cheryl Zhang
Edited by Joni Tan and Yvonne Choo

Contents

Irregular Time Signatures

A bar in irregular time is one which cannot be divided into equal groups of two or three beats.

The irregular times to be known in this grade are   (i) Quintuple time and   (ii) Septuple time.

Quintuple Time

There are 5 beats in every bar.

The grouping in quintuple time is (2 + 3) or (3 + 2) beats in a bar.

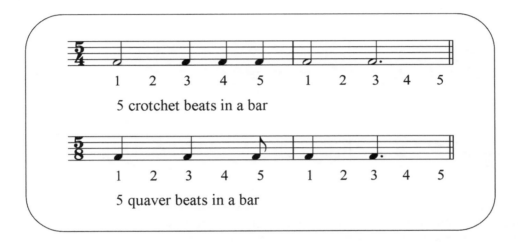

Septuple Time

There are 7 beats per bar.

The grouping in septuple time may be (2 + 2 + 3), (4 + 3), (2 + 3 + 2) or (3 + 2 + 2) beats in a bar.

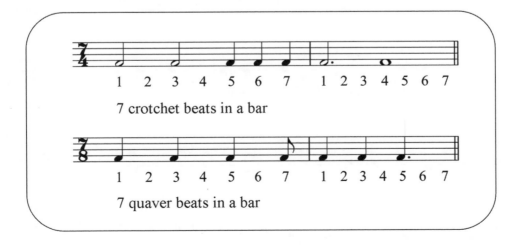

1. Add the correct irregular time signature to each of the following which begins on the first beat of the bar.

Copland, Music for the Theatre (2nd movt)

a)

Holst, The Planets Op. 32 (Neptune the Mystic)

b)

Falla, El Amor Brujo (Pantomine)

c)

Mussorsky, The Nursery

d)

L'Indy, Du Rythme Op. 68

e)

2. Add bar-lines to each of the following, which begins on the first beat of the bar.

Holst, The Planets (1st movt)

a)

Lekeu, Sonata in G for Viola and Piano

b)

Hindemith, Ludus Tonalis

c)

Holst, The Planets (Mars)

d)

Prokofiev, Piano Sonata No. 7

e)

3. The following passages begin on the first beat of the bar. However the time signatures change frequently. Add the time signatures where appropriate.

Bernstein, Jeremiah Symphony (3rd movt)

a)

© 1943 Reprinted by permission of Boosey & Hawkes Music Publishers Ltd.

Copland, Concerto for Orchestra and Piano (1st movt)

b)

© 1929 The Aaron Copland Fund for Music, Inc. Copyright Renewed. Boosey & Hawkes, Inc.,
Sole Licensee Reprinted by permission of Boosey & Hawkes Music Publishers Ltd.

Ireland, Sonata in G minor for Cello and Piano (1st movt)

c)

© Reproduced by permission of Stainer & Bell Ltd, London, England.

Bernstein, Fancy Free Ballet Variation 2

d)

© 1946 Reprinted by permission of Boosey & Hawkes Music Publishers Ltd.

Schumann, Symphony for Strings

e)

Stravinsky, Rite of Spring
(Mysterious Circles of the Adolescents)

f)

© 1912, 1921 by Hawkes & Son (London) Ltd. Reprinted by permission of Boosey & Hawkes Music Publishers Ltd.

Walton, Concerto for Violin and Orchestra (3rd movt)

g)

© 1945 Oxford University Press

Kudosa-Pillanant Kepek, Snapshots Op. 69

h)

Copland, Duo for Flute and Piano

i)

© 1971 by The Aaron Copland Fund for Music, Inc. Boosey & Hawkes, Inc., Sole Licensee
Reprinted by permission of Boosey & Hawkes Music Publishers Ltd.

Stravinsky, Rite of Spring

j)

© 1912, 1921 by Hawkes & Son (London) Ltd. Reprinted by permission of Boosey & Hawkes Music Publishers Ltd.

Irregular Time Divisions

Irregular divisions of a beat include **triplets** (in simple time) and **duplets** (in compound time).

A note can also be subdivided into irregular groups.

For example:

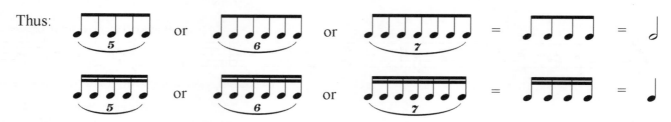

The principles of the subdivisions are such that :

(i)   A group of 5, 6 or 7 notes is played in the time of *a group of 4 of the same kind.*

Thus:

(ii) A group of 9 notes is played in the time of *a group of 8 of the same kind.*

Thus:

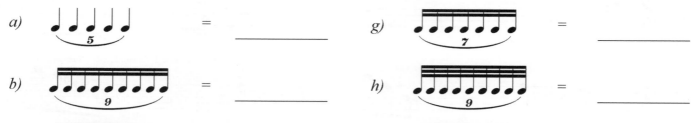

---

1.   Write a note to represent the time value of each of the following groups.

a) ⬤⬤⬤⬤⬤ 5   = _____   g) ⬤⬤⬤⬤⬤⬤⬤ 7   = _____

b) ⬤⬤⬤⬤⬤⬤⬤⬤⬤ 9   = _____   h) ⬤⬤⬤⬤⬤⬤⬤⬤⬤ 9   = _____

c) ⬤⬤⬤⬤⬤⬤ 6   = _____   i) ⬤⬤⬤⬤⬤⬤⬤ 7   = _____

d) ⬤⬤⬤⬤⬤⬤ 6   = _____   j) ⬤⬤⬤⬤⬤⬤ 6   = _____

e) ⬤⬤⬤⬤⬤⬤⬤ 7   = _____   k) ⬤⬤⬤⬤⬤ 5   = _____

f) ⬤⬤⬤⬤⬤ 5   = _____   l) ⬤⬤⬤⬤⬤ 5   = _____

2. Add bar-lines to each of the following which begins on the first beat of the bar unless otherwise indicated.

a) Brahms, Quintet in G Op. 111 (2nd movt)

b) Ireland, Trio No. 3 in E minor (3rd movt)

© Copyright 1938 by Hawkes & Son (London) Ltd.

c) Ravel, Tzigane for Violin and Orchestra

d) Schumann, Carnaval (Eusebius)

e) Paganini, Concerto No. 1 in D Op. 6

f) Sibelius, Symphony No. 1 (2nd movt)

© Breitkopf & Hartel, Weisbaden

g) Tchaikovsky, Symphony No. 5

h) Sibelius, Karelia Suite Op. 11

© Breitkopf & Hartel, Weisbaden

i) Sibelius, Symphony No. 4 (4th movt)

© Breitkopf & Hartel, Weisbaden

j) Walton, Concerto for Violin and Orchestra (2nd movt)

© 1945 Oxford University Press.

5

Tenor Clef

The tenor clef 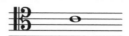 is one of the C clefs. The middle C lies on the 4th line.

Middle C

It can also be written as :    or   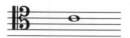

Do not confuse the alto and tenor clefs.

   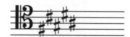

Tenor Clef   Alto Clef

The key signatures of up to 5 sharps and flats are arranged thus:

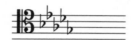

The tenor clef is used by the cello, bassoon and tenor trombone.

---

1. Write the letter names of these notes.

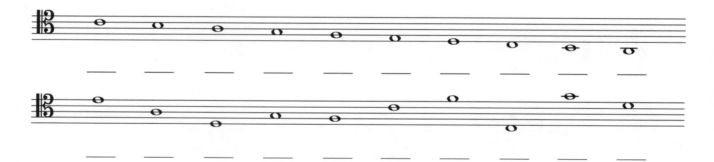

---

2. Write the letter names of each of the notes below, then rewrite them at the same pitch in the other clefs.

A flat

a)

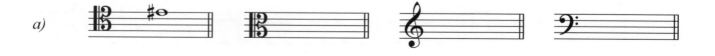

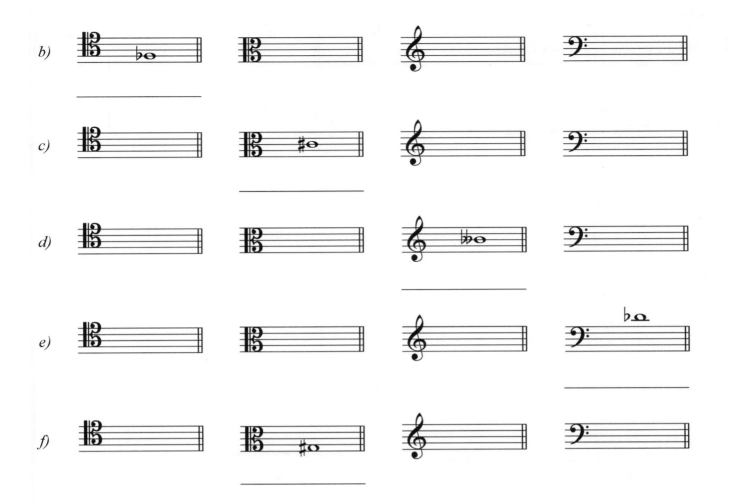

3. Using the tenor clef, write the required triad of each of the following keys. Use the correct key signature.

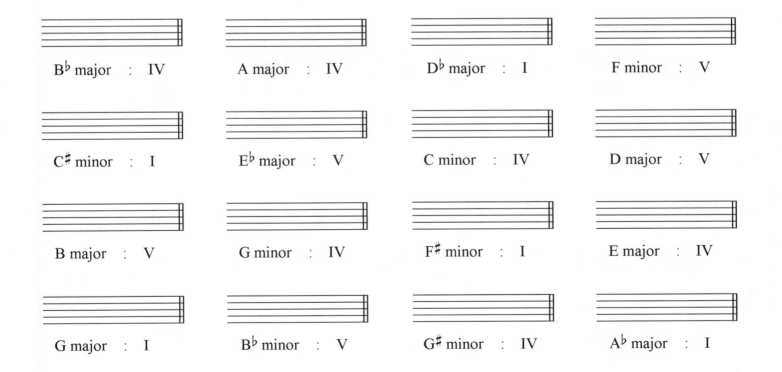

B♭ major : IV   A major : IV   D♭ major : I   F minor : V

C♯ minor : I   E♭ major : V   C minor : IV   D major : V

B major : V   G minor : IV   F♯ minor : I   E major : IV

G major : I   B♭ minor : V   G♯ minor : IV   A♭ major : I

4. Rewrite each of these passages using the tenor clef, keeping the pitch the same . (The opening of the first exercise has been shown.)

5. Rewrite these passages at the same pitch in the clefs required.

Major and Minor Keys

In Grade 5, major and minor keys of up to six sharps and flats are to be known. Here they are:

Major key	Key-signature	Minor key
C	-	A
G	F♯	E
D	F♯ C♯	B
A	F♯ C♯ G♯	F♯
E	F♯ C♯ G♯ D♯	C♯
B	F♯ C♯ G♯ D♯ A♯	G♯
F♯	F♯ C♯ G♯ D♯ A♯ E♯	D♯
F	B♭	D
B♭	B♭ E♭	G
E♭	B♭ E♭ A♭	C
A♭	B♭ E♭ A♭ D♭	F
D♭	B♭ E♭ A♭ D♭ G♭	B♭
G♭	B♭ E♭ A♭ D♭ G♭ C♭	E♭

The key signatures with six sharps and flats are written thus:

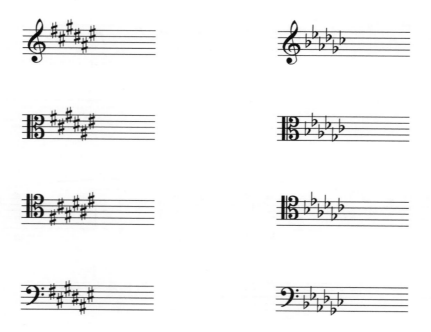

1. Add accidentals where necessary to form the scales named. Do not use any key signature.

a) E♭ melodic
minor

b) F♯ major

c) D♯ harmonic
minor

d) G♭ major

e) E♭ harmonic
minor

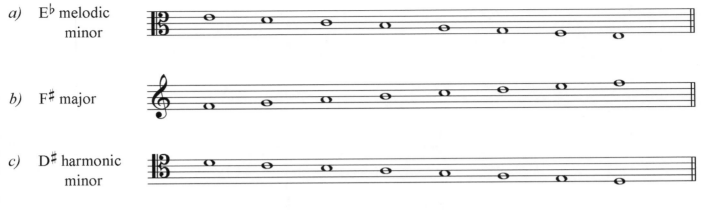

2. Using the correct key signatures and adding any necessary accidentals, write the following scales.
Use semibreves only.

a) D♯ melodic minor,
descending

b) G♭ major,
descending

c) F♯ major,
ascending

d) E♭ harmonic minor,
descending

e) D♯ harmonic minor,
ascending

f) E♭ melodic minor,
ascending

11

3. After the clefs, write triads as indicated in the given keys. Do not use key signatures but add any necessary accidentals.

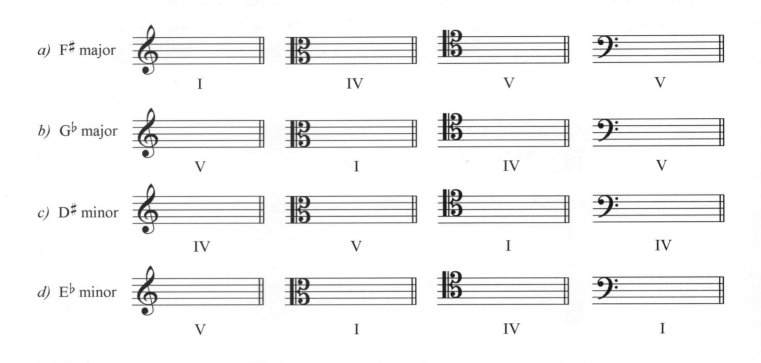

F♯ major and G♭ major are *enharmonic equivalents*. Both scales sound the same though the notes are written with different letter names.

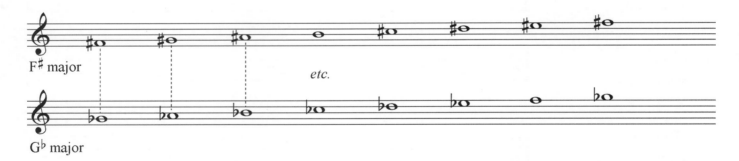

Likewise, notes of D♯ minor and E♭ minor are also enharmonic equivalents:

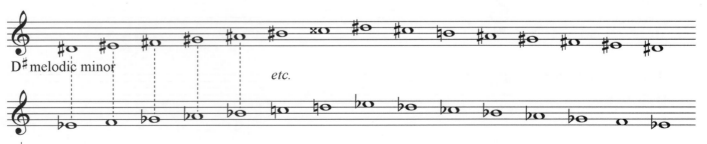

4. Name the key of each of the following scales. Without using any key signature, rewrite each of them in the enharmonic key. (An example is shown.)

Key: _____ G♭ major _____

Enharmonic key: _____ F♯ major _____

a)

Key: _____

Enharmonic key: _____

b)

Key: _____

Enharmonic key: _____

c)

Key: _____

Enharmonic key: _____

d)

Key: _____

Enharmonic key: _____

5. Rewrite the following passages using enharmonic equivalents. Change the key-signatures and letter names of the notes without changing the effect. (The answer to the first opening is shown.)

14

Supplementary Exercises

1. Add the correct clef and necessary accidentals to each of the following so as to form the scales named:

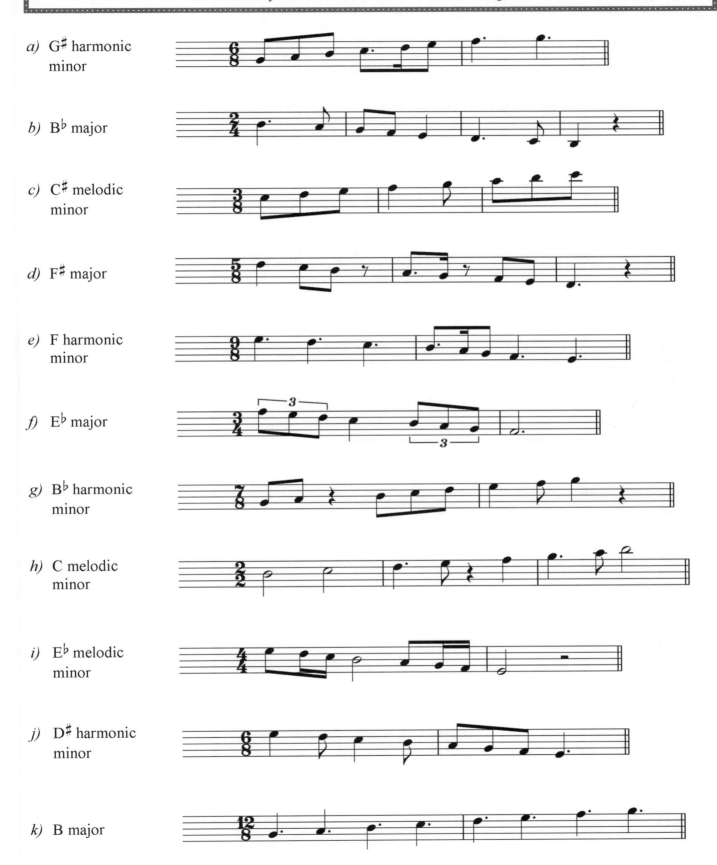

a) G♯ harmonic minor

b) B♭ major

c) C♯ melodic minor

d) F♯ major

e) F harmonic minor

f) E♭ major

g) B♭ harmonic minor

h) C melodic minor

i) E♭ melodic minor

j) D♯ harmonic minor

k) B major

2. Using the given rhythms, write each of the scales named. Complete the last bar marked * with a rest or rests.

a)

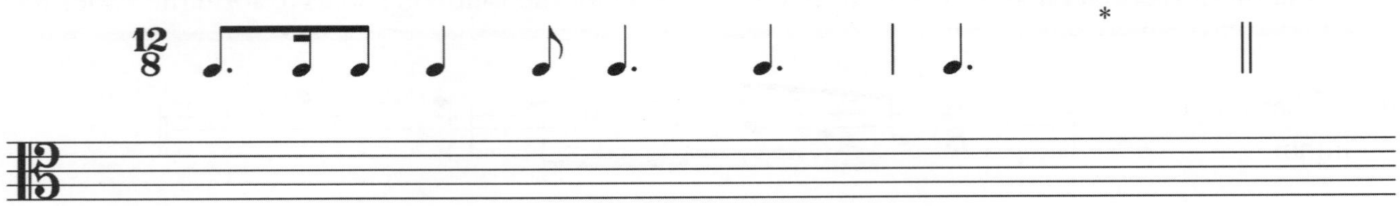

B♭ melodic minor, ascending, with key signature. Start on the mediant.

b)

A♭ major, descending, without key signature. Begin on the dominant.

c)

F♯ harmonic minor, ascending, without key signature. Begin on the dominant.

d)

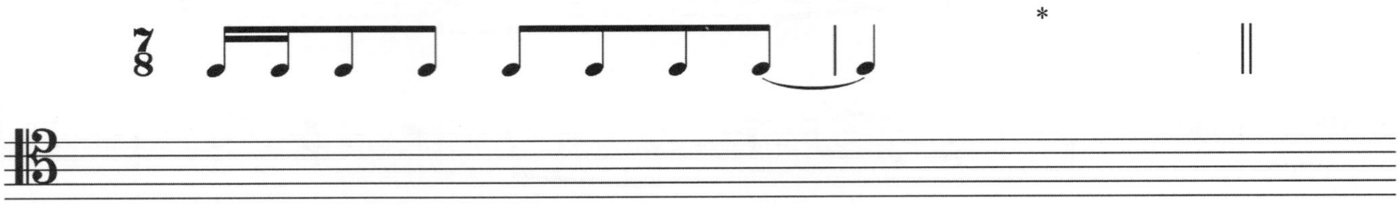

B major, ascending, with key signature. Begin on the subdominant.

e)

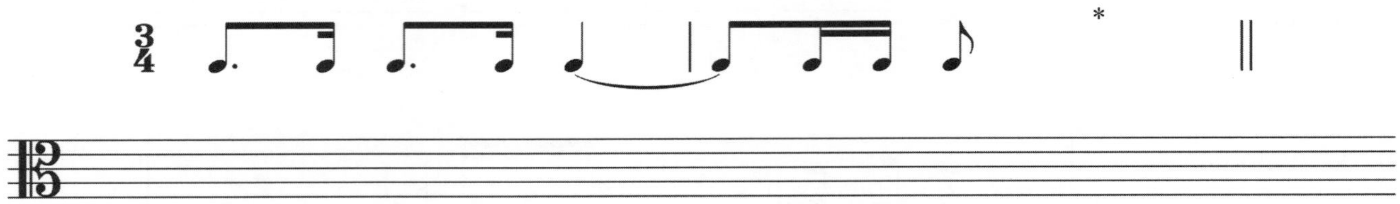

E♭ harmonic minor, descending, with key signature. Begin on the supertonic.

f)

D♯ melodic minor, descending, without key signature. Begin on the submediant.

3. Name the key of each of the following passages and then circle **any 3 notes within a bar** which form the tonic triad.

a) Grieg, Sonata Op. 45 No. 3

Key:_____

b) Faure, Elégie Op. 24

Key:_____

c) Bach, Prelude No. 13 (from the '48' Bk I)

Key:_____

d) Bach, Prelude No. 13 (from the '48' Bk I)

Key:_____

e) Haydn, Sonata

Key:_____

f) Beethoven, Rasumowsky Quartet

Key:_____

g) Moszkowski, Valse Mignonne

Key:_____

h) Brahms, Rhapsody Op. 79

Key:_____

i) Beethoven, Quartet Op. 127

Key:_____

Transposition

In Grade 5, the student will be required to transpose a melody up or down any one of the following intervals:

i) an octave   ii) a major 2nd   iii) a minor 3rd   iv) a perfect 5th

Transposing up or down an octave

As covered in grade 3, the transposition of a melody involves moving the notes an octave higher or lower using only the treble and bass clefs. In Grade 5, the student need to be able to transpose a melody using the alto and tenor clefs. Always ensure that the melody is transposed by *one octave* only.

        E.g.   Transpose this phrase down an octave using the alto and tenor clefs.

You may work out the first note before writing the transposed melody in the other clefs.

        Thus:

1. Transpose each of these passages *down an octave* into the given clefs.

b)

Mozart, Cosi fan tutte

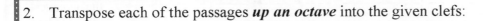

2. Transpose each of the passages *up an octave* into the given clefs:

a)

Franck, Symphony in D minor

b)

Berlioz, Romeo and Juliet

Transposition up or down a given interval

To transpose a given passage up a major 2nd

The Approach

1) Look at the key signature, then determine the key. Ignore the accidentals in the passage.

*The key signature suggests **F major**.*

2) Transposed up a major 2nd higher, , the new key is G major. Now shift all the notes accordingly by the numerical interval of a 2nd.

The new key signature, G major.

All notes are shifted up by the numerical interval of a 2nd.

3) Look at the accidentals in the original melody.

Now insert the corresponding accidentals into the transposed passage. They should be a major 2nd above the original.

Notes with accidentals are a major 2nd higher than the original

Take note:

If a melody is assumed to be in the **minor** key, the transposed melody is also made to the **minor** key.

*This suggests the key of **E minor**.*

Transposed up a major 2nd, , the new key is **F#minor**.

new key-signature

20

More examples:

Original melody

*suggests **F major**.*

i) **Transposed up a minor 3rd**   (, New key : A♭ major)

ii) **Transposed down a minor 3rd**   (, New key : D major)

iii) **Transposed up a perfect 5th**   (, New key : C major)

iv) **Transposed down a perfect 5th**   (, New key : B♭ major)

Take note that all notes with accidentals are transposed accordingly.

3. Transpose each of the following passages by the required interval. Insert the new key-signature and put in any necessary sharp, flat or natural signs. (The answer to the first opening is shown.)

Up a major 2nd

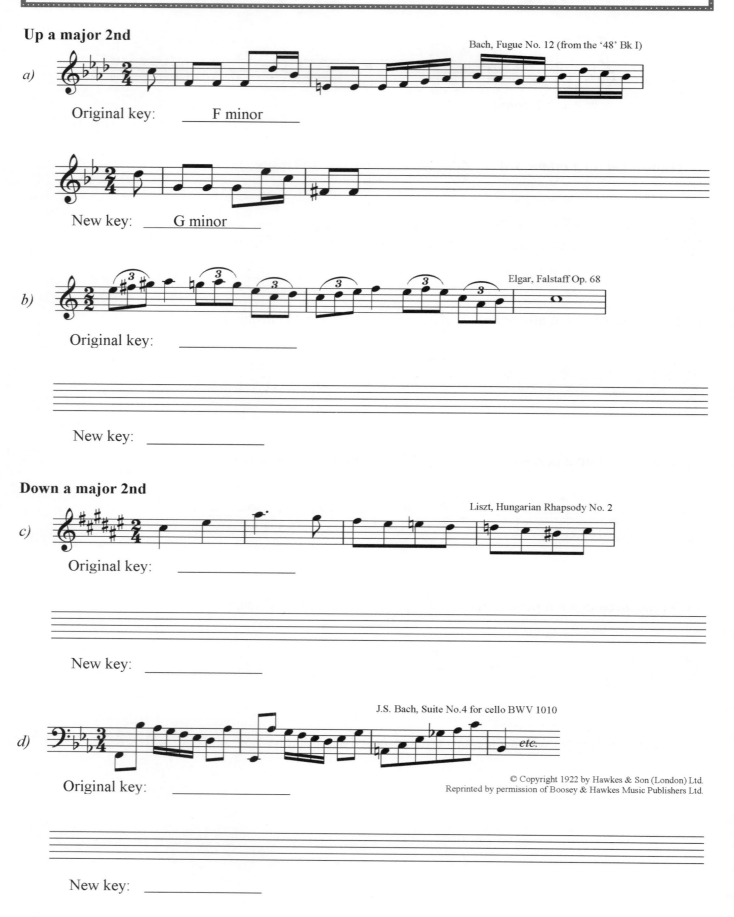

a)

Bach, Fugue No. 12 (from the '48' Bk I)

Original key: _____ F minor _____

New key: _____ G minor _____

b)

Elgar, Falstaff Op. 68

Original key: _____

New key: _____

Down a major 2nd

c)

Liszt, Hungarian Rhapsody No. 2

Original key: _____

New key: _____

d)

J.S. Bach, Suite No.4 for cello BWV 1010

etc.

Original key: _____

New key: _____

Up a minor 3rd

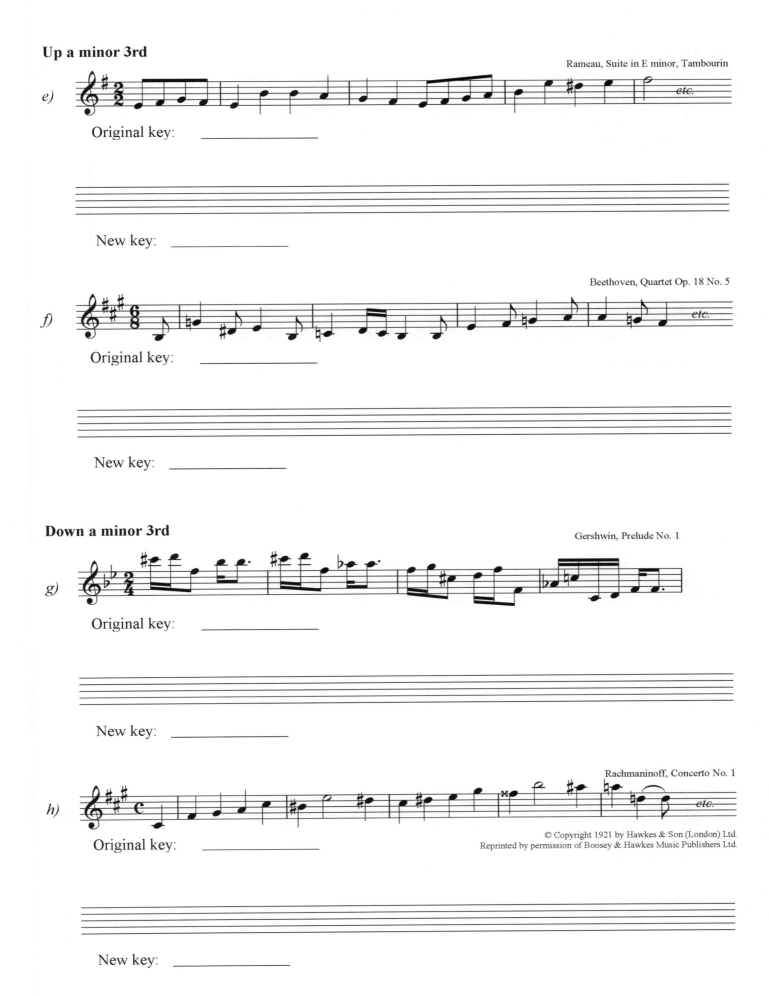

e)

Rameau, Suite in E minor, Tambourin

Original key: _____

New key: _____

Beethoven, Quartet Op. 18 No. 5

f)

Original key: _____

New key: _____

Down a minor 3rd

Gershwin, Prelude No. 1

g)

Original key: _____

New key: _____

Rachmaninoff, Concerto No. 1

h)

Original key: _____

New key: _____

Up a perfect 5th

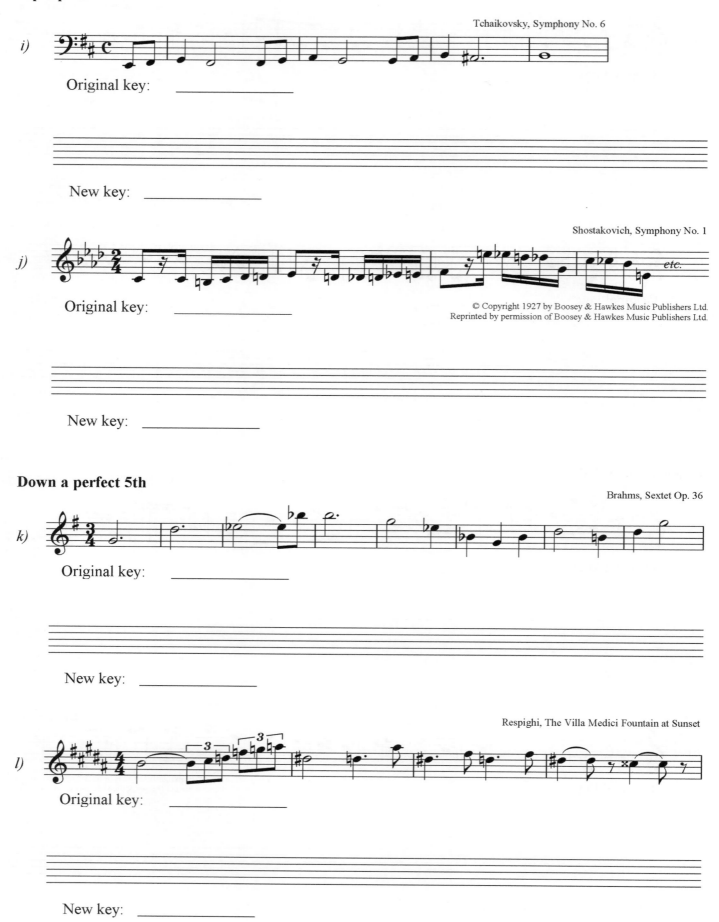

i) Tchaikovsky, Symphony No. 6

Original key: _____

New key: _____

j) Shostakovich, Symphony No. 1

Original key: _____

© Copyright 1927 by Boosey & Hawkes Music Publishers Ltd.
Reprinted by permission of Boosey & Hawkes Music Publishers Ltd.

New key: _____

Down a perfect 5th

k) Brahms, Sextet Op. 36

Original key: _____

New key: _____

l) Respighi, The Villa Medici Fountain at Sunset

Original key: _____

New key: _____

Transposing Instruments

Some instruments of the orchestra are transposing, that is they do not sound the notes as written but at an interval above or below the written notes.

Clarinet/Trumpet in B♭

When these instruments plays the written middle C, the note B♭ is produced, sounding **a major 2nd lower** than written.

Concert pitch refers to the pitch at which the music is actually heard.

Clarinet/Trumpet in A

When these instrument play the written middle C, the note A is produced, sounding **a minor 3rd lower** than written.

Horn in F/ Cor Anglais

When these instrument plays the written middle C, the F note is produced, sounding **a perfect 5th lower** than written.

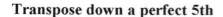

1. Transpose the following passages for the various instruments to sound at concert pitch. Use the correct key-signature and put in any necessary sharp, flat, or natural signs.

Transpose down a perfect 5th

Mozart, Concerto for Horn and Orchestra K417

a) Horn in F

Rimsky–Korsakov, Sniegourotchka

b) Cor Anglais

Transpose down a major 2nd

Edward Gregson, Prelude and Capriccio

c) Trumpet in B♭

Ferdinand David, Introduction, Theme and Variation

d) Clarinet in B♭

Transpose down a minor 3rd

Mozart, Clarinet Concerto K622

e) Trumpet in A

2. Rewrite the following passages as they would appear for the players of the various instruments. Do not use any key-signature but add any necessary sharp, flat, or natural signs.

Transpose up a major 2nd

a) Clarinet in B♭

Brahms, Sonata for Clarinet and Piano in F minor Op. 120 No. 1

b) Trumpet in B♭

Scriabin, Prelude Op. 8 No. 1

Transpose up a minor 3rd

c) Clarinet in A

Ravel, Le Tombeau de Couperin

d) Trumpet in A

Herbert Clarke, From the Shores of the Mighty Pacific

© Novello & Company Limited. Used by permission.

Transpose up a perfect 5th

e) Cor Anglais

Debussy, La Mer (II)

27

a)   Transpose a major 2nd lower for Clarinet in B♭.

Rimsky-Korsakov, Servilia

b)   Transpose a perfect 5th lower for Horn in F.

Delius, Walk to the Paradise Garden

c)   Transpose a minor 3rd lower for Trumpet in A.

Mendelssohn, The Hebrides

Intervals

At Grade 5, the intervals to be described may involve any two notes, including notes more than an octave apart. The lower note is not necessarily the key note. It would be useful to study the table below.

Interval		No. of semitones
Major	2nd	2
Major	3rd	4
Perfect	4th	5
Perfect	5th	7
Major	6th	9
Major	7th	11
Perfect	8ve	12

An **augmented interval** is one semitone larger than a major or perfect interval. Thus an augmented 5th contains 8 semitones.

A **minor interval** is one semitone smaller than a major interval. Thus a minor 7th contains 10 semitones.

A **diminished interval** is one semitone smaller than a perfect interval but two semitones smaller than a major interval. Thus a diminished 7th has 9 semitones and a diminished 5th has 6 semitones.

1. Describe the following intervals in full.

Minor 6th

2. Write a note above each of the following note so as to form the given intervals.

Augmented 5th	Minor 3rd	Diminished 7th	Major 2nd
Major 6th	Minor 7th	Augmented 7th	Diminished 4th
Minor 6th	Diminished 5th	Major 6th	Augmented 2nd
Perfect 4th	Augmented 4th	Major 7th	Perfect 8ve
Augmented 6th	Diminished 8ve	Diminished 3rd	Minor 2nd

Compound Intervals

Intervals that are more than 1 octave are called *compound intervals*. They can be described in 2 ways.

For example:

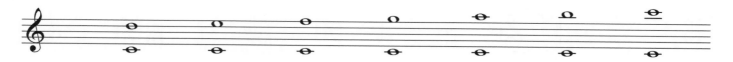

Description: Major 9th   Major 10th   Perfect 11th   Perfect 12th   Major 13th   Major 14th   Perfect 15th

OR   Compound   Compound   Compound   Compound   Compound   Compound   Compound
       Major 2nd   Major 3rd   Perfect 4th   Perfect 5th   Major 6th   Major 7th   Perfect 8ve

How do you determine the quality (i.e. major, diminished etc.) of any compound interval?

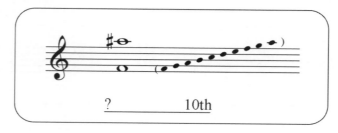

?_____10th

Shift one of the notes an octave closer to the other.

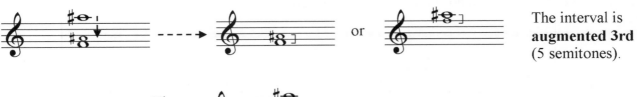

The interval is **augmented 3rd** (5 semitones).

Thus:

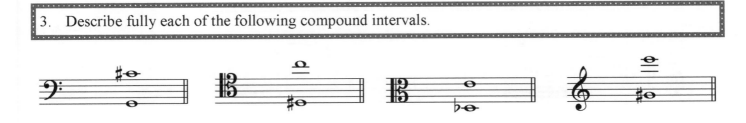

Augmented 10th (or compound augmented 3rd)

---

3.   Describe fully each of the following compound intervals.

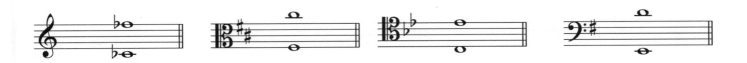

---

4.   Write the note above each of the following notes so as to form the compound interval named.

Major 13th	Perfect 12th	Perfect 11th	Minor 14th
Augmented 10th	Major 9th	Augmented 14th	Perfect 15th
Major 10th	Minor 13th	Diminished 11th	Augmented 9th

31

5. Describe each of the intervals marked ⌐⌐ in the following passages. Always describe an interval from the lower note to the higher one, no matter which one comes first. (The first answer has been given).

a)   Mozart, Symphony No. 1 (3rd movt)

1. ___Perfect 8ve___   3. _____

2. _____   4. _____

b)   Strauss, Salome Op. 54

1. _____   3. _____

2. _____   4. _____

c)   Bloch, Concerto Grosso

1. _____   3. _____

2. _____   4. _____

d)   Bruckner, Quintet in F

1. _____   3. _____

2. _____   4. _____

e)   Copland, Piano Variations

1. _____   3. _____

2. _____   4. _____

6. In the passages below, describe the intervals indicated by the dotted lines; take note of the key signature and other accidentals.

Bach, 2 Part Invention No. 15

a)

1. _____   2. _____   3. _____

4. _____   5. _____   6. _____

Bach, French Suite No. 2, Gigue

b)

1. _____   2. _____   3. _____

4. _____   5. _____   6. _____

7. In the passage below, describe the intervals marked with [ ] .

Beethoven, "Diabelli" Variations No. 30

1. _____   2. _____   3. _____

4. _____   5. _____   6. _____

7. _____   8. _____   9. _____

33

Vocal Scores

Most vocal works are written for a combination of 4 voices: Soprano, Alto, Tenor and Bass (S. A. T. B.). The music can be written either on a short score (2 staves) or on open scores (4 staves).

Short Score

Note:

(i) The treble stave is shared by Soprano (S) and Alto (A).

(ii) The bass stave is shared by Tenor (T) and Bass (B).

(iii) Each stave has its separate bar-lines.

(iv) The stems of the notes for (S) and (T) always go up, and those for (A) and (B) go down.

(v) For two voices that share 1 stave, an accidental that occurs in 1 voice must be written in the other even if it occurs within the same bar. *

Open Score

The above passage can be transcribed into open score.

Note:

(i) Each of the 4 voices is written on a separate stave with separate bar-lines.

(ii) The tenor part is written an octave higher with a small *8* under the treble clef to show that it sounds an octave lower than written.

1. Transcribe each of the passages below into short score. (The solution to the opening of the first example is given.)

a)

Boyce, I was glad

b)

Giovanni Croce, Is It Nothing To You?

35

c)

John Dryden, Ah fading joy, how quickly art thou past!

d)

Phyllis Tate, Album Leaf

36

2. Transcribe the following passages into open score. (The answer to the first opening is given.)

a)

Werlé, Spring and Fall

b)

Elgar, The Shower

c)

Michael Burnett, Nowell Sing We Both
All and Some

d)

Gerard Schürmann, Summer is Coming

Identify Chords

At Grade V, the chords to be known are:

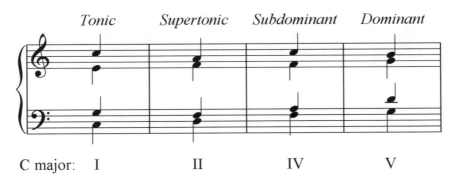

The student also needs to identify the position of a chord, that is, whether the *root, 3rd or 5th* of the chord is in the bass.

The tonic chord of C major may be written in 3 positions:

Description	Tonic Chord in root position (root in the bass)	Tonic Chord in 1st inversion (3rd in the bass)	Tonic chord in 2nd inversion (5th in the bass)
Roman Numerals	I or Ia	Ib	Ic
Figured bass notation:	$I\frac{5}{3}$	$I\frac{6}{3}$	$I\frac{6}{4}$

In the exercises to follow, the student may indicate his chords by using any **ONE** of the following methods:

1)   Roman numerals i.e. I, II, IV, V

2)   Notations used in jazz and popular music e.g. Dm, Gm

3)   Figured bass e.g.

4)   Write out the notes in full on the staves.

1. Name the key of each of the passages and then identify the numbered chords.

a)

Key: _____

1. _____
2. _____
3. _____
4. _____
5. _____
6. _____

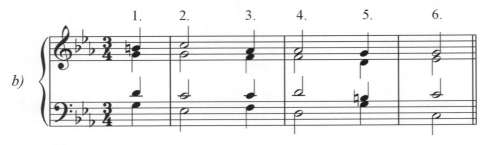

b)

Key: _____

1. _____
2. _____
3. _____
4. _____
5. _____
6. _____

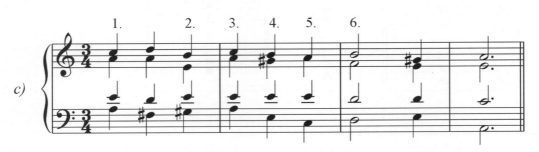

c)

Key: _____

1. _____
2. _____
3. _____
4. _____
5. _____
6. _____

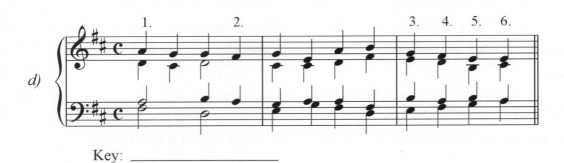

d)

Key: _____

1. _____
2. _____
3. _____
4. _____
5. _____
6. _____

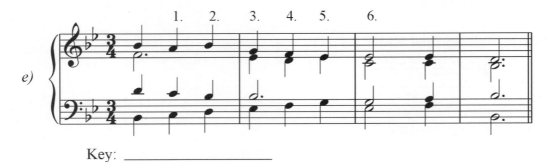

e)

Key: _____

1. _____
2. _____
3. _____
4. _____
5. _____
6. _____

2. Identify the key and the chords marked * in each of the following passages.

Eric Thiman, O, No John

a)

Key: _____   _____   _____   _____   _____

Mendelssohn

b)

Key: _____   _____ _____   _____   _____ _____

J.S. Bach, Chorale "Allein Gott in der Hoh' sei Ehr"

c)

Key: _____   _____ _____ _____ _____   _____ _____

Beethoven, Piano Sonatas Op. 10

d)

Key: _____   _____   _____   _____

J.S. Bach, Chorale "Sollt' ich meinem Gott nicht elugen"

e)

Key: _____   _____ _____ _____ _____   _____

Key: _____   ___   ___

Key: _____   ___   ___

Key: _____   ___   ___   ___

Key: _____   ___   ___   ___   ___

Key: _____   ___   ___   ___

42

Cadences

Cadences normally occur at the end of phrases. Each cadence consists of 2 chords. At Grade 5, only the chords I, II, IV and V (all in root position) are used. The cadences to be known are:

All examples are in C major

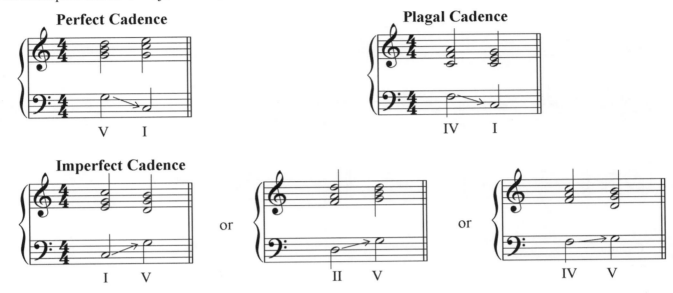

1. In each of the following, choose suitable chords to form cadences. Name the cadence in each case. (A working stave has been provided.) Only the keys of C, G, D and F majors are used.

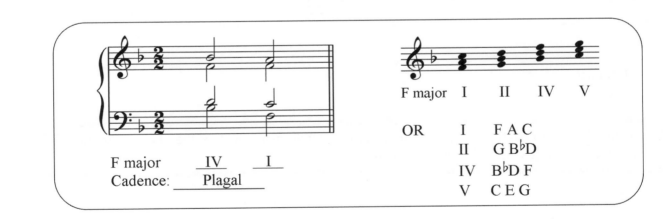

F major _____IV_____ _____I_____
Cadence: _____Plagal_____

F major   I   II   IV   V

OR   I   F A C
          II   G B♭D
         IV   B♭D F
          V   C E G

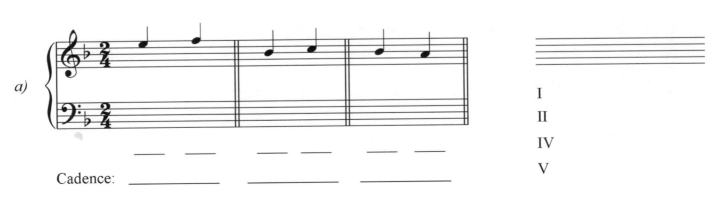

a)

I

II

IV

V

Cadence: _____ _____ _____

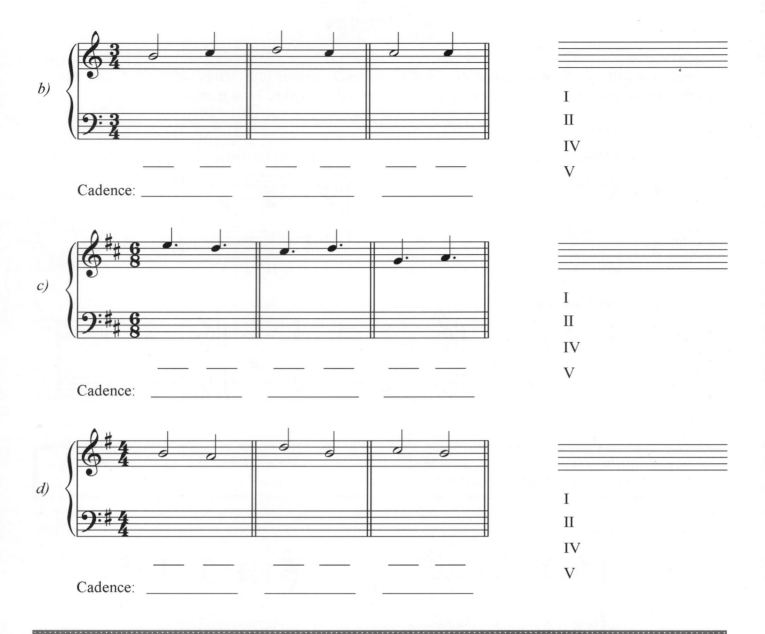

b)

Cadence: _____   _____   _____

I
II
IV
V

c)

Cadence: _____   _____   _____

I
II
IV
V

d)

Cadence: _____   _____   _____

I
II
IV
V

2. Name the key of each of the following passages. Underneath each of the places marked `*    *` choose 2 suitable chords to form cadences.

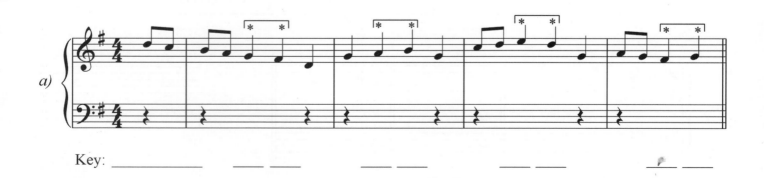

a)

Key: _____   ___ ___   ___ ___   ___ ___   ___ ___

b)

Key: _____ __ __ ____ _____

c)

Key: _____ ____ ____ ____ ____ ____ ____

d)

Key: _____ ____ ____ ____ ____

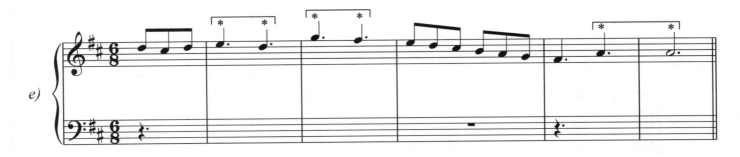

e)

Key: _____ ____ ____ ____ ____

45

Harmonising Cadences

In a musical passage, it is not always the case where one melodic note is harmonized by one chord.

i) A long note may be harmonised by 2 chords:

C major   V   I

ii) A chord may be used to harmonise more than 1 note:

F major   I   V

iii) Passing notes and auxiliary notes are not to be harmonised. They do not belong to the chords.

Passing Note:

G major   V   I

A *passing note* lies between 2 harmony notes on either side, one above and one below it.

Auxiliary Note:

C major   V   I

An *auxiliary note* occurs between the repetition of a harmony note. The harmony note may be a step above or below.

46

3. In each of the following passages, suggest suitable chords for the places marked 1.└─┘ 2.└─┘ etc. You do not need to indicate the position of the chords or state which note is in the bars. Show the chords EITHER (i) by writing I, II, IV, V OR (ii) by writing notes on the staves. Use only one method.

e)

f)

g)

h)

Composing a Melody

At Grade 5, the student will be required to compose a melody of not more than 8 bars either for an instrument or for voice. When writing for an instrument, take note of the following points:

i)   Specify the instrument of your choice.

ii) Bear in mind the range of each particular instrument and its characteristics.
     For example, string instruments may play pizzicato notes. Instruments such as the cello, horn and trombone usually play slow moving passages.

iii) Choose the correct clef appropriate for the instrument. For example, the viola may use the alto clef and the trombone may use the tenor clef.

Elements of Melodic Writing

The Rhythmic Structure

i)   Write an 8-bar rhythm divided into 2 halves, each ending with a relatively long note. *Remember, the given bars are to be counted.*

ii) Make use of repetitions where appropriate. (See Grades 2 and 3 on "Four bar rhythms"):

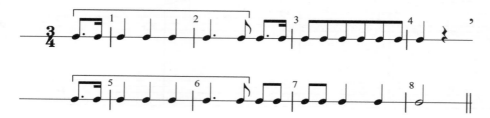

Notice in the above, *the opening of the 1st half is repeated in that of the 2nd half.*

The Melodic Structure

The student may consider the following points to construct the melody.

i)   **Exact repetition**

Where an opening rhythm repeats itself, the same notes may also be repeated:

Brahms, Symphony No.4

ii)   **Modified Repetition**

To avoid boredom, the repetition may be slightly modified; that is, to repeat the same rhythm using different notes:

Beethoven, Symphony No.6

A rhythmic repetition may also occur with the notes at a degree higher or lower:

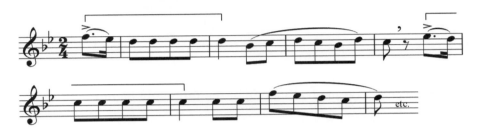

iii)   **Sequence**

A melodic figure may be repeated immediately with all the notes moving up (or down) by 1 degree:

Schubert, Wanderer

iv)   **Movement of notes**

a)   The melody should have a sense of direction or shape. It may move towards a high point (a climax) and then down again. Avoid moving aimlessly around the same few notes.

b)   Use scalic movement at most times. Leaps are good for contrasts; but avoid too many of them, otherwise the melody may lose its shape.

c)   Avoid dissonant intervals such as the augmented 2nd and the augmented 4th as they create dissonant effects.

The diminished 5th interval may be used but it should resolve melodically within its compass:

d)   When writing in the minor key, it is advisable to use the melodic form.

Cadences

End the first half of the melody on an imperfect cadence i.e. on a note of the dominant chord (V).
The final note should be the tonic itself:

Suggested Endings

Do not leap abruptly towards the end. You may adopt one of the following endings:

(The numbers correspond to the movable solfege system.)

Final points

Include all performance directions:

i)   Phrases, slurs and articulation marks (e.g. staccato marks, bow marks.)

ii)   Tempo direction (e.g. Allegro, Andante, ♩ = **100**)

iii) Dynamics (e.g. **p**, **f**, *cresc*, *dim.*)

1. Compose a complete melody of not more than 8 bars for each one of the following openings. Circle your choice of unaccompanied instrument. Indicate the tempo and other performance directions, including any that might be particularly required for the instrument chosen.

a)

Choice of instrument: violin/ trumpet/ clarinet.

b)

Choice of instrument: oboe/ horn/ clarinet.

c)

Choice of instrument: cello/ bassoon/ trombone.

d)

Choice of instrument: violin/
        clarinet/
        trumpet.

e)

Choice of instrument: cello/
        bassoon/
        trombone.

f)

Choice of instrument: violin/
        clarinet/
        flute.

g)

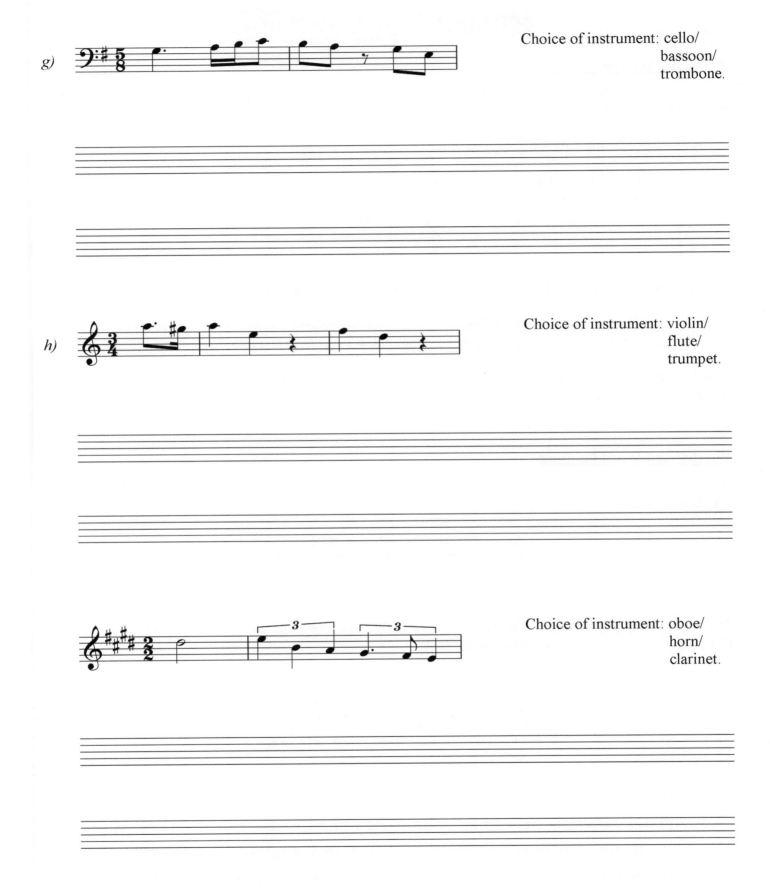

Choice of instrument: cello/
bassoon/
trombone.

h)

Choice of instrument: violin/
flute/
trumpet.

Choice of instrument: oboe/
horn/
clarinet.

Setting a Melody to Words

Principles of a Good Setting

The basic principles of melodic writing outlined in the previous chapter apply likewise in setting words to music. However, there are a few differences.

i)   The opening bars are not given.

ii) Voices have smaller ranges compared to instruments, therefore it would be advisable to write within this range:

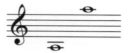

iii) Wide leaps are to be avoided as they are unsuitable for singers.

iv) The rhythm should be kept simple with at least one note to a syllable. The tempo marking chosen must also be appropriate. For example, *presto* is too fast to be sung.

Consider the words when writing for the voice, which in themselves suggest musical ideas such as rhythm, the mood and melodic shape.

Rhythm and Word Painting

In setting words to music, the rhythm is determined by the natural speech rhythm with accents falling on the main beats.

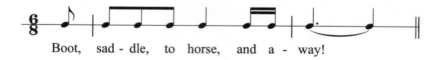

Boot, sad - dle, to horse, and a - way!

The contour, key and rhythm of the melody should reflect the mood and character suggested by the words. It is possible to apply 'word painting' to the text:

Boot, sad - dle, to horse, and a - way!

(i)   The galloping effect of the horse is reflected in the choice of G major and the $\frac{6}{8}$ time.

(ii) The melodic leaps of a 6th for 'to horse' and a 5th for 'a-way!' ending on a long note are effective in creating the visual impact and lively spirit suggested by the words.

(iii) The rising melodic contour based on the tonic triad gives a strong sense of key and thus certainty and sense of confidence to the phrase.

The Structure

In writing the melody, a good structure is needed to achieve a sense of unity. It is a common practice to divide the verse into 2 equal parts, each containing 2 phrases. The use of rhythmic repetition is recommended. (See Grade 3: Simple Phrase Structure.)

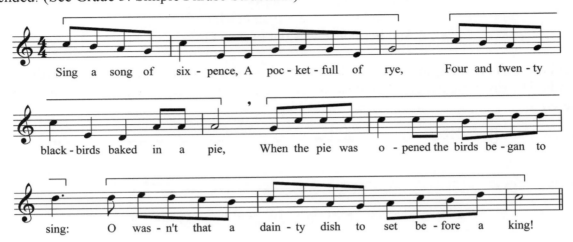

In the above example, the opening rhythm ♩♩♩♩ | ♩ is repeated at the beginning of the 2nd and 3rd phrases.

However, if certain phrases or words are repeated, the student may repeat only that portion of the melody.

Whittaker, Oh! rest thee, babe

The Melodic Shape

A melody must reveal a shape, a contour i.e. it should have a sense of direction. Certain words in the poem may suggest a possible high point in the melody. Such a 'climax' should be given both length and height within the melodic curve.

For example:

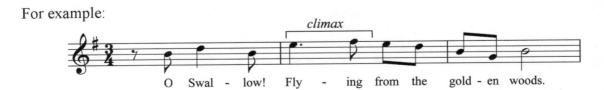

Setting a Stanza to Music

For example:

> Old Meg she was a Gypsy,
> And lived upon the moors:
> Her bed it was the brown heath turf,
> And her house was out of doors.

Step 1: Read through the lines, marking out the accented syllables. Next write a suitable rhythm for the words. The rhythmic pattern should show some regularity and coherence. Some repetitions are preferred.

Step 2: Now compose the melody bearing in mind the following:

i) A cadence must be suggested at the end of each phrase; often by a long note or rest.
ii) Use repetitions or sequences to achieve unity.
iii) Locate the climax suggested by the words which may (though not always) occur in the 3rd line.
iv) Sing the melody as you write. Avoid writing a melody that is pointlessly complicated.

Step 3: Indicate the tempo and other performance directions as appropriate.

A setting need not be "syllabic": i.e. each syllable with one note. You may introduce the use of melisma i.e. 2 or more notes to a syllable to make the melody interesting. Here is the melodic setting for the example discussed in Practice in Music Theory Grade 4.

58

1. Compose a complete melody to each of the following. Write each syllable clearly under the note or notes to which it is to be sung. Indicate the tempo, dynamics and other performance directions as appropriate..

a)   Sweet day, so cool, so calm, so bright
The bridal of the earth and sky
George Herbert

b)   Sweet was the sound, when oft at evening's close
Up yonder hill the village murmur rose.
Oliver Goldsmith

c)   A land of streams! Some, like a downward smoke,
Slow-dropping veils of thinnest lawn, did go.
Lord Tennyson

d)   The night is chill, the cloud is gray:
'Tis a month before the month of May.

John Keats

e)   A violet by a mossy stone
Half hidden from the eye!

William Wordsworth

f)   The night is chill, the cloud is gray:
'Tis a month before the month of May.

John Keats

g)   The rusted nails fell from the knots
        That held the pear to the garden-

Lord Tennyson

h)   I bear light shade for the leaves when laid
        In their noonday dreams.

Percy Bysshe Shelley

i)   My heart is at rest within my breast,
        And everything else is still.

Anonymous

Ornaments

1. Name the ornament sign used in each of the following:

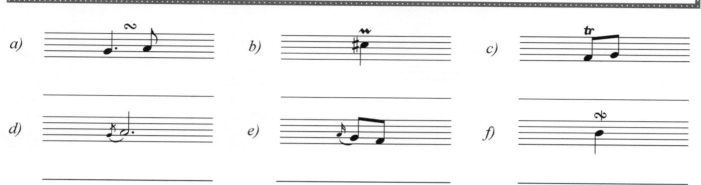

a) _____

b) _____

c) _____

d) _____

e) _____

f) _____

2. Copy out the melody, replacing the notes under each of the brackets ⌐‾‾⌐ with the appropriate ornament sign. Refer to Appendix I for a list of ornaments and how they are to be played.

63

Musical Terms

The following are additional musical terms to be studied by the student at Grade 5. Learn to pronounce the Italian and German terms and then memorise their meanings. The complete lists of foreign terms and signs for Grade 5 are included in the Appendix II and III of this book. Study them before attempting the exercises that follow. For more terms, see Appendix II on page 78 to 83.

Italian Terms

Attacca	go on immediately
Dolente	sadly
Dolore	grief, sorrow
Doppio movimento	double the speed
Estinto	as soft as possible, lifeless
Incalzando, incalcando	getting faster and louder
Lacrimoso	tearfully
Loco	at the normal pitch (used to cancel an *8va* direction)
Lunga	long
Lunga pausa	long pause
Lusingando	coaxing, in a sweet and persuasive style
Misura	measure
Alla misura	in strict time
Senza misura	in free time
Ossia	or, alternatively
Piacevole	pleasant
Piangevole	plaintive, in the style of a lament
Pochettino, poch	very little
Rinzforzando, rf, rfz	reinforcing
Segue	go straight on
Smorzando, smorz.	dying away in tone and speed
Teneramente, tenerezza	tenderly, tenderness
Tosto	swift, rapid
Volante	flying, fast
Zart	tender, delicate
Zu	to, too

German Terms

Aber	but
Ausdruck	expression
Bewegt	with movement, agitated
Breit	broad, expansive
Ein	a, one
Einfach	simple
Etwas	somewhat, rather
Fröhlich	cheerful, joyful
Immer	always
Langsam	slow
Lebhaft	lively
Mässig	at a moderate speed
Mit	with
Nicht	not
Ohne	without
Ruhig	peaceful
Schnell	fast
Sehr	very
Süss	sweet
Traurig	sad
Und	and
Voll	full
Wenig	little
Wieder	again

Italian Terms

Explain the meaning of the Italian terms below.

1. **On Tempo**

    doppio movimento _____

    incalzando _____

    tosto _____

    volante _____

2. **On Performance Direction**

    attacca _____

    loco _____

    lunga pausa _____

    rinforzando, rf, rfs _____

    segue _____

    pochettino (poch.) _____

    misura _____

    alla misura _____

    senza misura _____

3. **On Expression / Style**

    dolente _____

    dolore _____

    doloroso _____

    estinto _____

    lacrimoso _____

    lusingando _____

    piacevole _____

    smorzando (smorz.) _____

    teneramente _____

    tenerezza _____

German Terms

Explain the meaning of the German terms below:

1. **On Tempo**

   langsam _____

   mässig _____

   schnell _____

2. **On Performance style**

   Ausdruck _____

   Ausdrucksvoll _____

   bewegt _____

   breit _____

   einfach _____

   fröhlich _____

   lebhaft _____

   ruhig _____

   süss _____

   traurig _____

   zart _____

3. **Other Terms**

   aber _____

   ein _____

   etwas _____

   etwas traurig _____

   immer _____

   immer lebhafter _____

   mit ped _____

   nicht zu langsam _____

   ohne ped. _____

Rest and Repetitions

1. Explain the following signs for rests. Refer to Appendix III.

_____

_____

2. Write out in full how each of the following should be played.

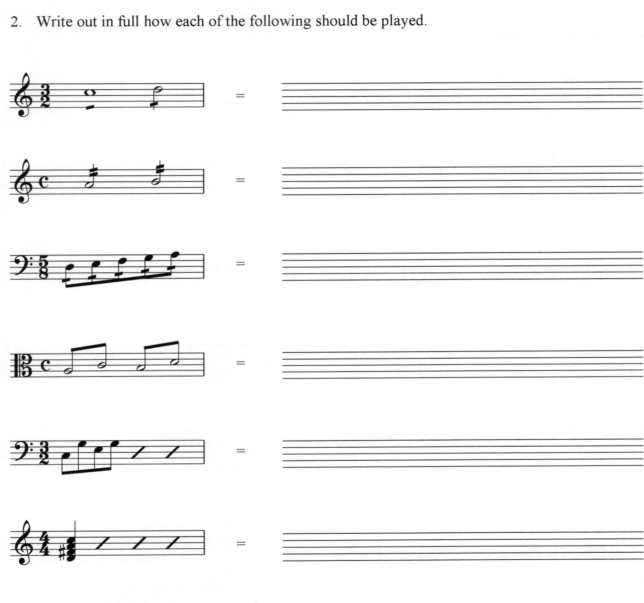

General Exercises

1. This is the *Adagio for Two Horns and Bassoon K410* by Mozart. Look at it, and then answer the questions that follow.

a) The first 4 bars are in F major. Using roman numerals, indicate the chords used in bar 4 (marked with *) and name the cadence.

Name of cadence: _____

b) The opening of the 1st horn has been marked with a ⌐￢ . Mark similarly whenever the same rhythm occurs in another instrument.

c) In which bar does a chromatic scale occur? Bar_____ . Instrument:_____

d) Name the intervals marked (i), (ii) and (iii).

(i) _____ (ii) _____ (iii) _____

e) Complete the following sentences.

The bassoon is a _____ reed instrument. Besides the bass clef it may also use the

_____ clef. It belongs to the _____ family which also include standard

members such as the _____ , the _____ , and the _____ .

f) Name another orchestral instrument which can play the bassoon part. _____ .

g) The horns here are at concert pitch. Transpose the 1st horn part from bars 1-4 up a perfect 5th, to its written pitch. Do not use a key-signature, but remember to include all necessary sharp, flat or natural signs.

2. This excerpt is from Rimsky-Korsakov's Opera *The Tsar's Bible*. Look at it and then answer the questions below.

a) Which 4 instruments are playing the extract?

_____ , _____ , _____ and _____ .

b) To which family do the instruments belong? _____

Name the other 2 standard instruments of the same family. _____ , _____

c) Why do the 2 staves use different key-signatures?

_____

d) Rewrite bars 5 to 8 in open score. Transpose the clarinet parts down a major 2nd as they would sound at concert pitch. Use the correct key signature and any necessary accidentals.

e) The key of the extract is F major. Use the open score written above to describe the chords marked (i), (ii) and (iii) as I, II, IV or V. Also indicate whether the lowest note of the chord is the root, 3rd or 5th.

(i) _____   (ii) _____   (iii) _____

f) Describe the intervals marked ⌐x and ⌐y in bars 2 and 7.

⌐x _____   ⌐y _____

g) Name the ornament sign found at bar 8.

_____

h) Explain the following terms:

Allegretto _____

♩=*112* _____

dim. _____

mf _____

3. This passage is a reduction from the 2nd movement of Haydn's Trumpet Concerto in E♭. Look at it and then answer the questions that follow.

a) Name the key of this passage. _____

b) Give the meaning of the following terms:

Andante _____

expressivo _____

cantabile _____

piu **p** _____

c) Choose a suitable speed from the following and then write it at the appropriate place.

♩ = **40**   ♩. = **60**   ♩ = **80**   ♪ = **120**

d) Complete the sentences:

The trumpet belongs to the _____ family. At concert pitch, trumpet in B♭ sounds

_____ lower than written. Three other transposing instruments of the orchestra are

the _____ , the _____ and the _____ .

e) What can you say about the melody at bars 5 and 6 as compared to bars 1 and 2?

_____

f) Describe the chords marked ☐ in bars 2, 4, 7 and 8.

(i) _____   (ii) _____

(iii) _____   (iv) _____

Specimen Test

Duration 2 hours

Total Marks
100

This paper contains SEVEN questions, ALL of which should be answered.
Write your answers on this paper - no others will be accepted.
Answers must be written clearly and neatly - otherwise marks may be lost.

1 (a) Add a rest or rests at each of the places marked * to complete the bar.

10

(b) Write a four-bar rhythm in **7/8** time, beginning as shown.

2 Write out at concert pitch the following melody written for trumpet in B♭.
The interval of transposition is a major 2nd lower.

10

Georges Hüe, Contest Pieb

3 (a) Give the full name of this scale.

10

Scale ————————

(b) Rewrite the above at an octave lower using the tenor clef. Use the key signature and add any essential accidentals.

4 (a) Write the key signature of the keys named below.

10

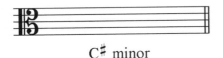

C♯ minor

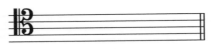

E♭ minor

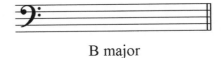

B major

(b) Describe fully each of the intervals and also name a key in which each may be found.

Interval _____   Interval _____

Key   _____   Key   _____

5 (a) Describe each chord marked * as I, II, IV or V. Also indicate their positions.   `15`
       i.e. whether the root, third or fifth is in the bass.

   (b) Underneath the last 2 notes, write a suitable chord for each. You may use I, II, IV or V
       or any recognized method of notation.

   _____   _____   _____   (1)____ (2)____

6 EITHER
                                                                       `15`

   (a) Write a melody for violin or flute using the given opening. Add marks of
       tempo, expression and other performance directions suitable for the instrument
       chosen. The melody should not be more than 8 bars.

                                          Choice of instrument: _____

   OR

   (b) Compose a melody for the following words. Write each syllable under the note or notes to which it
       is to be sung.

                        In the earth - thou shalt be laid,
                        A stone standing over thee.
                                          Emily Bronte

74

7 This extract is from the Notturno of Borodin's String Quartet No. 2.
Look at it and then answer the questions below.

30

(a) *(i)* Give the meaning of the following:

    Andante _____

    pp *dolce* _____

    cant. col espress. _____

    fp _____

  (ii) Name the ornament used in bar 2. _____

(b) *(i)* The passage is written for a string quartet. Write the correct names of the instruments used, before the staves of this extract.

  (ii) How can the instrument on the 3rd stave play two notes at the same time? Name the term used.

    _____

  (iii) What do the terms 'pizzacato' and 'arco' mean in string music?

    _____

(c) *(i)* Describe the intervals marked x ⌈ , y ⌈ and z ⌈ in bars 2, 5 and 6.

    (x)_____ (y) _____ (z)_____

  (ii) Using the tenor clef, transpose the bass part of bars 1 to 3 an octave lower. Include the key signature, time signature and dynamics.

Appendix I - List of Ornaments

Name & Sign	Description	Examples in Performance
Acciaccatura	A small quaver with a stroke slurred to the main note. It can be played in 3 ways.	(i) Played just before the beat. (ii) Played on the beat with the accent on the main note. (iii) Played with the main note but released immediately.
Appoggiatura	A small note which "leans" against another.	(i) It takes half the value of the main note (ii) It takes two-thirds the value of a dotted note.
Turn	This usually consists of 4 notes – *note above, main note, note below, main note.* (You may remember it as)	(i) The note values may be equally divided or the first 3 notes may be faster. (ii) The turn may occur after a note.
Inverted turn (Lower turn)	Like the turn, this consists of 4 notes, but in the reverse direction – *note below, main note, note above, main note.*	(i) The note values are similar to the turn. (ii) An inverted turn may occur after a note.

Name & Sign	Description	Examples in Performance
Mordent ~~	The main note alternates with the higher note.	
Inverted mordent/ Lower mordent ~~	The main note alternates with the lower note	The division of note values are similar to the mordent.
Trill/Shake *tr* or *tr*~~~~	It consists of a continuous alternation between the *upper* and *main* note in a rapid manner.	(i) At a moderate or slower tempo the note values are usually demisemiquavers. (ii) At a quick tempo fewer notes can be played; often notated as semiquavers.
Arpeggiation {	A wavy sign placed before a chord.	(i) The notes are to be played starting on the beat, from the lowest, spreading upwards like an arpeggio as quickly as possible, with the entire chord held at the end.

Appendix II - List of Musical Terms

A (à)	at, to, by, for, in the style of
Aber	but
Accelerando	becoming gradually faster
Adagietto	rather slow
Adagio	slow, leisurely
Adagissimo	very slow
Affetuoso	tenderly
Affrettando	hurrying
Agitato	agitated
Alla	in the style of
Alla Marcia	in the style of a march
Alla polacca	in the style of a polonaise
Allargando	broadening out
Allegretto	slightly slower than allegro
Allegro	lively, reasonably fast
Allegro assai	very quick
Amabile	amiable, pleasant
Andante	at a walking pace
Andantino	quite slow
Animato	lively, animated
Animé	animated, lively
Appassionata	with passion
Assai	very
Assez	enough, sufficiently
Attacca	go on immediately
A tempo	in time
Ausdruck	expression
Avec	with
Bewegt	with movement, agitated
Bravura	with boldness and spirit
Breit	broad, expansive
Brillante	sparkling, brilliant
Cantabile	in a singing style
Calando	dying away, getting slower and softer

Calando	dying away, getting slower and softer
Cédez	yield, relax the speed
Col; Con	with
Con anima	with deep feeling
Con brio	with vigour
Con moto	with movement
Con spirito	with spirit, life, energy
Crescendo, cresc.	becoming gradually louder
Da capo, D.C.	from the beginning
Dal segno, D.S.	repeat from the sign 𝄋
Deciso	with determination
Decrescendo, decresc.	becoming gradually softer
Delicato	delicately
Diminuendo, dim.	becoming gradually softer
Dolce	sweetly
Dolcissimo	very sweetly
Dolente	sad, mournful
Doloroso	sorrowful
Doppio movimento	twice as fast
Doppio	double
Douce	sweet
Ein	a, one
Einfach	simple
En dehors	prominent
Energico	with energy
Espressione	expression
Espressivo, Espress., Espr.	with expression, feeling
Et	and
Etwas	somewhat, rather
Facile	easy
*Fortepiano, **fp***	loud, then immediately soft
Fine	the end
*Forte, **f***	loud
*Fortissimo, **ff***	very loud

Forza	force, power
Forzando, fz	with a strong accent
Fröhlich	cheerful, joyful
Fuoco	fire
Furioso	furiously
Giocoso	merry
Giusto	exact, proper
Grandioso	in a grand manner
Grave	very slow
Grazioso	gracefully
Immer	always
Langsam	slow
Largamente	in a broad style
Larghetto	slower than largo
Largo	slow and stately, broad
Lebhaft	lively
Legatissimo	as smoothly as possible
Legato	smoothly
Légérement	lightly
Lent	slow
Lento	slowly
L'Istesso	the same
Ma	but
Ma non troppo	but not too much
Maestoso	majestically
Mais	but
Marcato	marked, accented
Martellato	hammered out
Marziale	in a military style
Mässig	at a moderate speed
Meno	less
Meno mosso	less movement
Mesto	sadly
Mezzo forte, mf	moderately loud

80

Mezzo piano, **mp**	moderately soft
Misterioso	mysteriously
Mit	with
Moderato	at a moderate pace
Modéré	at a moderate speed
Moins	less
Molto	much
Morendo	dying away
Mosso	movement
Moto	movement
Movimento	movement
Nicht	not
Niente	nothing
Nobilmente	nobly
Non	not
Non tanto	not so much
Non troppo	not too much
Ohne	without
Parlando	in a speaking manner
Parlante	in a speaking manner
Pastorale	in a pastorale style
Patetico	with feeling
Perdendosi	dying away
Pesante	heavily
Peu	little
Piano, **p**	soft
Pianissimo, **pp**	very soft
Piu	more
Pizzicato, pizz.	plucked
Plus	more
Poco a poco	little by little
Possibile	possible
Presto possibile	as fast as possible
Presser	hurry

En pressant	hurrying on
Prestissimo	as fast as possible
Presto	very quick
Quasi	as if, resembling
Ralentir	slow down
Rallentendo, rall.	becoming gradually slower
Retenu	held back
En retenant	holding back
Risoluto	boldly
Ritardando, ritard. rit.	gradually slower
Ritenuto, riten. rit.	hold back, slower at once
Ritmico	rhythmically
Ruhig	peaceful
Sans	without
Scherzando	playfully
Scherzo	a joke
Schnell	fast
Semplice	simple
Sempre	always
Senza	without
Sforzando, **sf**, **sfz**	with a sudden accent
Simile, sim.	in the same way
Slargando	becoming gradually slower
Slentando	becoming gradually slower
Smorzando	dying away
Sonoro	with rich tone
Sopra	above
Sospirando	sighing
Sostenuto	sustained
Sotto	below
Sotto voce	in an undertone
Spiritoso	lively, animated
Staccatissimo	very detached
Staccato	short, detached

Stringendo	becoming gradually faster
Subito	suddenly
Süss	sweet
Tanto	too much
Tempo	speed, time
Tempo comodo	at a comfortable speed
Tempo primo	resume the original speed
Tempo rubato	with some freedom of time
Tenuto	held on
Tranquillo	quietly
Traurig	sad
Très	very
Triste, Tristamente	sad, sorrowful
Troppo	too much
Tutti	all
Und	and
Veloce	swift
Vibrato	vibrating
Vif	lively
Vite	quick
Vivace, Vivo	lively, quick
Vivacissimo	very lively
Voce	voice
Voll	full
Volta	time
Prima volta	first time
Seconda volta	second time
Volti subito, V.S.	turn the page quickly
Wenig	little
Wieder	again

Appendix III - List of Musical Signs

⌢ or ⌣ as in 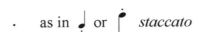 or **slur**

⌢ as in  **tie**

⌒ over several notes **phrase**

. as in ♩. or ♩̇ *staccato* short, detached

‥‥ as in **portato** the notes are to be slightly detached

> as in ♩> or ♩^> **accent**

▾ as in ♩ or ♩ *staccatissimo* very short, often with accent

· as in ♩. or ♩· the note is lengthened by half its value

·· as in ♩.. or ♩·· the note is lengthened by three-quarter of its value

⌢ or ⌣ as in ♩ or ♩ *fermata* pause on the note

– as in ♩ or ♩̄ *tenuto* held or to play with emphasis

𝄆 and 𝄇 the passage is to be repeated

♩ = 66 or ♩ = c.66 66 crotchet beats to the minute
or MM. ♩ = 66

< getting gradually louder

> getting gradually softer

▬ bar rest

rest for 7 bars

 Ped. ✳ to depress the damper pedal of the piano and release at the sign ✳

Reiterated Notes

A single stroke indicates use of reiterated or repeated quavers.

Two strokes indicate reiterated or repeated semiquavers.

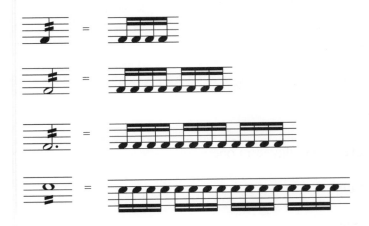

Alternation of Notes

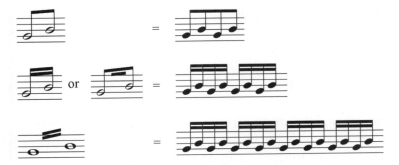

85

Appendix IV - Orchestral Instruments

The String Family

All the instruments in this section have 4 strings. Usually the strings are played with the bow. Sometimes the strings are plucked, is called *pizzicato*. If the players are to return to the normal way of playing with the bow, the instruction *arco* is used.

Instrument	Clef(s) used	Notes tuned to:
Violin	treble	G D A E
Viola	alto or treble	C G D A
Violoncello or Cello	bass or treble or tenor	C G D A
Double Bass	bass	E A D G sounds an octave lower

Commonly Used Terms and Signs for String Instruments

⊓	down bow
V	up bow
(slur symbol)	slur, notes to be played in one bow
con sordini, con sord.	with mutes
senza sordini, senza sord.	without mutes
pizzicato, pizz.	pluck the string
arco	to play with the bow (a direction after pizzicato)
sul G	play on the G string
sul ponticello	play near the bridge
tremolo (note symbols)	to quiver rapidly on the string to create a trembling effect
double stopping (note symbol)	to play 2 notes together with one bow
harmonic (note symbol)	A note to be played as a harmonic sounds an octave higher with a 'whistling' and fainter effect

The Woodwind Family

In a woodwind instrument, sound is produced when air is blown through a hollow tube that causes vibrations. There are 4 standard instruments in the woodwind family. The clarinet is transposing. It does not sound the written pitch, but at an interval above or below the given notes.

Instrument	Clef(s) used	Transposing?	Type of reed used
Flute	𝄞	No	None
Oboe	𝄞	No	Double
Clarinet	𝄞	Yes	Single
Bassoon	𝄢	No	Double

The Brass Family

Sound is produced in a brass instrument when air passes through a mouthpiece and vibrates in the tube. The pitch of each note produced is controlled by the pressure exerted by the lips. With the exception of the trombone which uses the slide, all the other brass instruments use valves or pistons to vary the tuning of the notes.

Instrument	Clef(s) used	Transposing?
Trumpet	𝄞	Yes, except for trumpet in C
Horn	𝄞 or 𝄢	Yes
Trombone	𝄢 or 𝄡	No
Tuba	𝄢	No

The Percussion Family

Sound is produced when a percussion instrument is struck, hit or shaken. Usually, percussion instruments are classified into definite or indefinite pitch.

Instruments with definite pitch	Instruments with indefinite pitch
Timpani	Bass drum
Xylophone	Side drum
Glockenspiel	Cymbals
Marimba	Triangle
Celesta	Gong
Tubular bells	Tambourine

Best-Selling Titles

Practice in Music Theory Grade 6
Revised Edition
by Josephine Koh

This revised edition of *Practice in Music Theory* Grade 6 is part of the highly recommended theory coursebooks for students preparing for the ABRSM examinations. It is the first of three comprehensive coursebooks that guide students toward achieving a high standard of knowledge in harmony, counterpoint, melodic writing and score analysis that spans almost four centuries of Western musical history. The *J Koh's* instructional approach here is academic, yet musically conceived with ample musical illustrations and examples. The mastery of the basic principles of harmony is presented in Part I, while Part II introduces students to the more creative realm of compositional techniques and score analysis.

Scales and Arpeggios for Piano
J Koh's Fingering Method

Students can now learn scales and arpeggios in the most enjoyable and effective way. *J Koh's Fingering Method* develops the learners' technical skills by using a combination of visual, auditory and tactile systems. Now available in print, this proven method used for training gifted children is specially produced to assist students prepare for the ABRSM graded piano practical examinations. Success assured! The series from Grades 1 to 5 focuses on establishing good fingering habits. The *Fingering & Tonality Method* for Grades 6 to 8 continues the development of technical competence in piano students based on key and chord structures.

Available from Grades 1 to 8.

Teachers' Choice, Selected Piano Repertory
Examination Pieces for 2009-2010 Series
Edited and Annotated by Josephine Koh

A refreshing new publication which comprises popular and alternative works from the ABRSM Piano Examination syllabus. These pieces are specially selected to provide students with a comprehensive and varied repertoire. Meticulously fingered and edited, *Teachers' Choice* offers teachers and students alike added performance and teaching directions. Scores in *Teachers' Choice* are beautifully set and annotated for excellent reading.

Available from Grades 1 to 8.